GW00391505

Originally published in 1892, this
wisdom for 'The Lady's Dressing Room'
offers timeless advice for discerning
women today who are planning
a room of their own.

THE
LADY'S
DRESSING ROOM

Beauty and relaxation secrets

Copper Beech Publishing

Published in Great Britain by
Copper Beech Publishing Ltd
This edition © Copper Beech Publishing Ltd 2003
Edited by Julie Hird and Jan Barnes

ISBN 1-898617-32-5
A CIP catalogue record for this book is available from The
British Library.

THE PREPARATIONS IN THIS BOOK, ALTHOUGH
RECOMMENDED FOR WOMEN YEARS AGO, ARE
NOW OFFERED HERE FOR HISTORICAL INTEREST.
NO GUARANTEES ARE OFFERED AND NO
LIABILITY TAKEN.

Copper Beech Gift Books
Copper Beech Publishing Ltd
PO Box 159 East Grinstead
Sussex England RH19 4FS

CONTENTS

Introduction

In her dressing room a lady can lose herself and there she practises all kinds of magic, in order to keep herself astonishingly young and lovely!

The woman who knows this makes of her dressing room, a sanctuary where no one, not even her husband (above all, not her husband) may cross the threshold. It is there that she faces the effects of time and the fatigues of life.

A woman should always be found fresh, beautiful and sweet as a flower; everyone should believe her to be so adorned by nature, like the lilies of the field. No-one need know that her beauty is acquired at the cost of a thousand little attentions.

What is life, without some illusions?

Smooth over any wrinkles, create an amiable frame of mind and find the fresh and beautiful you with this advice from 1892.

LUXURY AND COMFORT

The dressing room of every well-bred woman should be both elegant and comfortable in proportion to her fortune and position.

A lady's dressing room may be simply comfortable, but it should still be elegant and must have everything necessary to a careful toilette.

Walls and floors

Some dressing rooms have their walls entirely covered with tiles, but the effect is cold to sight and touch. Walls should be in neutral tints, so as not to clash with the colours of your dresses. The pearl-grey carpet should have a design of either roses or lilac.

Lights

From the ceiling should hang a small lustre to hold candles and care should be taken to place wide bobeches on the candles, to prevent any danger of wax falling on the dresses.

INDISPENSABLE ACCESSORIES

No slop-buckets or water-cans should be seen ...

There must be two tables, opposite to each other, of different dimensions, but the same shape.

The larger table

A larger table is meant for minor ablutions; on it should be placed a jug and basin chosen with taste and care. Above this table should run a shelf, on which are placed the bottles for toilet waters and vinegars, perfumes, glass, etc. At either side of the basin should be placed the brush and soap trays and the sponges.

The smaller table

The smaller table bears the mirror, should be framed in a ruche of satin and lace; the table itself is draped. This table is for the art of hairdressing, so everything necessary must be found upon it. This must include boxes for hair-pins, and a large casket for the brushes and combs.

Perfume

The following should also have their places on the smaller table:

Bottles of perfume
Scented oil
Powder boxes
Manicure case

Fireplace

The fireplace should occupy the centre of the wall opposite the window; a Dresden clock and some vases of fresh flowers should be placed upon it. At one side of the fireplace should be placed a chaise-longue in blue or mauve damask, (the pattern being in white). About the room a few arm-chairs will be found convenient.

Wardrobes

At either side of the dressing-table there should be a wardrobe. The ordinary wardrobe with a single panel of glass has been banished from all artistic bed-rooms and dressing rooms.

The first should have three mirrors in its doors. The side doors open at opposite angles, and thus form a triple-sided, full-length mirror, in which one can judge the effect of both dress and coiffure from all points of view.

The second wardrobe, which should be lacquered too, has no mirror, its doors being painted with garlands of flowers. In it are placed the reserve stock of bran, starch, soaps, powder, creams, etc.

Slops

No slop-buckets or water-cans should be seen, nor should any other paraphernalia be visible; everything of that kind should be hidden from sight in special closets or cupboards near at hand.

If the dressing-room does not adjoin the bath-room, the tub should be brought each day into the dressing room for the daily sponge bath.

A MORE SIMPLE STYLE

You can ornament your wardrobe yourself.

A dressing room may be much more simple. All excess of luxury may be suppressed, but a woman of taste can still create a little sanctuary both elegant and tasteful.

Walls and floors
A pretty wall-paper should be chosen, and the floor covered with an oil-cloth.

Tables
Drape deal tables with wide flounces edged with frills of the same material; cover the tables with linen toilet-cloths edged with deep thread lace, and on them place the washing utensils in bright coloured ware. If the tables are small, have shelves made and cover in the same style as the tables to accommodate your bottles and boxes.

Wardrobes
If your mirror is somewhat ordinary, you can hide its frame under a pleated frill, fastened on with small tacks. You can ornament your wardrobe yourself, painting and varnishing it to match the room, and your own individual fancy.

Shelves
If it is necessary to keep your dresses, your bandboxes, your boots and shoes, in your dressing room, have some shelves placed across the end of the room at a sufficient height to allow you to hang your dresses from hooks. On these shelves you can put your boxes and parcels.

Hide with curtains
The whole should be hidden by curtains to match the draperies of the tables. These curtains should not be placed against the wall, as they would then reveal the outlines of all the things they are meant to hide! They should be hung from the ceiling, and enclose the shelves as in an alcove; behind them also may be placed the bath-tub.

THE BATH ROOM

A couch where one reposes after the fatigues of the bath.

The bath room is often part of the dressing room. The walls can be panelled with coloured onyxes, framed in copper mouldings, which must be polished every day. From the ceiling hang chandeliers and from a golden rod, hang a curtain, to veil the bath of rose-coloured marble.

After the bath
At the opposite side of the room is placed a couch where one reposes after the fatigues of the bath. In one corner, screened from view by a silken curtain, are the apparatus for the shower, or other kind of spray bath.

A large basin is accompanied by another smaller one and both are painted with designs of water-lilies and aquatic plants.

Have small shelves of marble for all the other articles required when bathing.

LOOFAHS SOAPS AND CREAMS

Beauty aids ... should be hidden from the eye.

All the beauty aids - the linen, the loofahs, soaps, creams, cosmetics and perfumes - should be hidden from every eye, as no one likes to be suspected of adventitious aids. All dresses put out of sight in wardrobes and closets.

A mat for the bath

Before each bath should be placed a mat in leather, or cork, whereon the bather may stand. Near the bath, shelves should be fastened to the wall to carry the necessary soaps and sponges.

Other supplies

A wardrobe should contain a supply of bath-linen, fine towels, bath-sheets, the various kinds of soaps, the boxes of starch, the bags of bran, the perfumes, almond paste and cold creams.

Besides the actual bath, there should be in the bath-room a couch or ottoman, whereon to repose after the bath; and a little table, in case one would wish to have a cup of tea.

SOOTHING AND REFRESHING BATHS

*Regular bathing should enter into the
habits of all classes of society.*

If it is impossible to immerse oneself completely
every day, a sponge bath is sufficient.

A cold bath
Some people immerse themselves every day in a
cold bath. It is wise to consult a doctor. When
allowed, take only one cold plunge and come out
at once. The water should be 50 to 60 degrees.

A tepid bath
The tepid bath is most used and the temperature
may range from 68 to 96 degrees. It is a mistake
to remain too long; fifteen to thirty minutes is
the maximum time one should stay therein.

A hot bath
The hot bath is good for those who are subject
to a rush of blood to the head.

Beauty secrets for bathing

The healthy action of stimulating the pores
of the skin by the bath, especially if it is
followed by friction with a flesh-glove
or a rough towel, is very energising.

~

A hot bath is known to have worked surpris-
ing cures in cases of obstinate constipation.

~

Anyone who is afraid of having caught a
contagious malady should immediately have
recourse to a hot bath, as it is quite possible
that the infection may make its way out
of the body through the pores.

~

Cleanliness of the skin is said to have a great
effect in the proper assimilation of
nourishment by the body.

A good rubbing - and other rules

A good rubbing is a necessity after every bath. It is often a good thing to take a little air and exercise after the bath, but only on condition of walking very fast.

Never take a bath, or in any way immerse yourself in water, immediately after having eaten. Even minor ablutions are apt to trouble the digestion. One should allow three hours to elapse between any meal and a bath.

When soap is used in a large bath, it should be used towards the end of the time of immersion, and should be immediately washed off with clear water.

The soap chosen should be white and very pure, and little, if at all, perfumed.

It is contrary to cleanliness and hygiene that two people should bathe in the same water.

Soothing and refreshing baths

In spring, it is best to take one's bath at night, just before going to bed, to avoid all possibility of a chill. The skin may benefit by the moist warmth which it will thus be able to keep for several hours after having left the water.

A cowslip and primrose bath in spring time

A delicious bath for this season can be prepared with cowslips and primroses. Three handfuls of these flowers, freshly gathered, should be thrown into the bath, which thus becomes delightfully perfumed, but extremely calming to the nerves by the virtue in the sweet golden petals.

A strawberry and raspberry bath

A bath of strawberries and raspberries is prepared in the following manner:- Twenty pounds of strawberries and two of raspberries are crushed and thrown into the bath, from which the bather emerges with a skin freshly perfumed, soft as velvet, and tinged with a delicate pink.

A lime flower bath
A bath of lime flowers (a delightful perfume) is particularly soothing to over-excited nerves.

A spinach bath
A decoction of spinach makes an excellent bath for the skin.

Fresh and delicate skin
A recipe equally good for rendering the skin fresh and delicate:-

   60 grammes of glycerine,
   100 grammes of rose-water,
   mix with two quarts of water.

Add to the bath five minutes before using it.

Other recipes
Some women mix almond-paste with their bath, and perfume it with violet.
Others prefer oatmeal and orange-flower water.
Others prefer tincture of benzoin, which gives the water a milky appearance.

A bran bath

Two pounds of bran, placed in a muslin bag, are allowed to soak in a small quantity of water for three hours before the bath.

Aromatic salts and essences easily prepared

This is easily prepared. Pound into powder some carbonate of soda and sprinkle it with some aromatic essences (of which only a small quantity is needed). These aromatic essences can be prepared beforehand, according to the following recipe:-

Essence of fine lavender	15 grammes
Essence of rosemary	10 grammes
Essence of eucalyptus	5 grammes
Carbonate of soda crystals	600 grammes

Pound the cystals, sprinkle and mix them with the essences, and keep them in a well-stoppered bottle. For a large bath, 315 grammes of this aromatic salt will be required; for a basin, a teaspoonful to a quart of water.

A bath for the exhausted nervous system
Mix one ounce of ammonia to a bucket of water. In a bath of this kind the flesh becomes as firm and smooth as marble, and the skin is purified in the most perfect way.

A bath for rheumatism sufferers
The following bath should ease the pain of those who suffer from rheumatism:
A concentrated emulsion should be made with 200 grammes of soft soap and 200 grammes of essence of turpentine. Shake well together, until the mixture is in a lather. For a bath, take half this emulsion, which has an agreeable smell of pine when mixed with the water. At the end one should leave the bath, and get straight into bed, and gently fall asleep. On waking in the morning, the pain is greatly alleviated.

Massage to create a sense of well-being
The masseuse kneads all the muscular parts of
the body and this excites the vitality of the spirit.
Massage must follow the bath, not precede it.
When the skin is moist, it is naturally more
supple and is more easily kneaded. The patient
can feel fatigue after the massage, but this is followed by a sense of well-being and vivacity.
Care should be taken, however, not to make an
abuse of massage - for if it is over-done, its effects are exhausting rather than strengthening;
but in certain climates and in certain maladies,
there is no doubt it is very beneficial.

Rubbings to increase vigour
In many cases judicious rubbings are an excellent substitute for massage. It is best to use for
these frictions a flesh-glove.
Nothing is better, after a foot-bath or a sponge
bath, than a vigorous rubbing; it increases the
force and vigour of the body, benefits the gen-
eral health, and is an admirable aid to beauty.

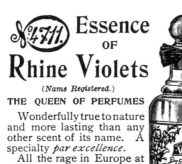
After the dry-rubbing, all the body should be rubbed with a piece or a band of flannel dipped in toilet-vinegar or perfume.

How to clean sponges

Nothing is so horrible and disgusting as a sponge that looks grey and dingy, even if it be not really dirty. A sponge in this state should be steeped in milk for twelve hours. After this time, rinse it in cold water, and it will be as good as new, minus the expense. Lemon-juice is also excellent for whitening a sponge.

Important details

One may also have recourse at first to carbonate of soda, which sometimes proves sufficient. These are small but very important details, over which the mistress of the house should herself keep watch, for servants think them unworthy of their attention.

CLEANLINESS

"Cleanliness is half a virtue and uncleanliness
the second half."
Alexandre Dumas

Want of cleanliness is an ugly and ignoble vice, and it is incompatible with the desire to be beautiful and beloved.

The importantance of well-washed skin

Cleanliness is as indispensable to health as it is to beauty. A woman who keeps the pores of her skin open by the daily use of cold or tepid water, will keep well and grow old slowly. But under the closed pores of a skin not well or frequently washed, the flesh becomes flabby and soft.

A well-washed skin is smooth, silky, and fresh; but if repeated layers of perspiration and dust are allowed to accumulate, the skin becomes dry and feverish.

For numbers of people it is not possible to take baths every day.

If a lady cannot spare these few moments every day to take an entire bath, at least she might take time for a partial one, certain parts of the body requiring more care than others!

At least once a week

Once a week at the least, the necessary time for taking a complete bath should be made. This is the very minimum of washing that our bodies absolutely require. As for the maximum of cleanliness, there is no limit on this point.

Self-respect

We are wanting in self-respect if we fail to keep rigorously clean and neat, and nature will punish us for such neglect by premature old age. Bathing and washing, assisted by good soaps, and even vinegars and perfumes, will make our bodies firm, fit and capable of endurance. Water has the virtue of dissipating all fatigue and giving us pure bodies.

*A sponge bath only requires a few moments
of time and a quiet corner.*

Quiet, sufficient sleep, and walks in the rain,
are said to be perfect for beauty.

THE FACE

Encounter a downpour without an umbrella.

The pores of the skin should be kept open, and washing is the best means of keeping them free from the secretions which might clog them.

When the weather is warm

It is bad to wash in cold water when the weather is very warm, or when the face is much heated either by natural or artificial warmth. Tepid water should be used, with lotions, but without soap. The face should then be slightly powdered, and allowed to dry without being wiped.

A fine and rather worn towel

When drying the face do so gently, with a fine and rather worn towel. Friction with a hard towel will thicken the skin.

*The face requires as delicate care as a precious
piece of porcelain or a fine work of art!*

The prettiest women

The prettiest women in society plunge a towel
into very hot water, wring it out, and lay it on
their faces for half-an-hour. Try this before getting into bed, wiping off lightly any dust that
may have collected there during the day.

At the age of fifty

A woman of fifty whose skin is as smooth as
that of a young girl, has never washed her face
except with extremely hot water which, she de-
clares, tightens the skin and destroys wrinkles.
It has also been suggested that the face should
be washed in water in harmony with the exter-
nal temperature; in winter wash your face with
cold water, in summer, with warm or tepid water and so on.

Beauty secrets - for the face

Half an hour should be allowed to pass after
washing, before going out, or sitting at
an open window.

~

The face should never be bathed in too
violent a manner.

~

It may sometimes be necessary to use soap for
the face. In this case the soap should be very
carefully chosen. Never use soap when the
weather is very warm.

~

Lemon-juice cleans the skin very well, and
is much better than soap.

~

Strawberry-juice has the same detergent action
and is, moreover, very good for the skin.

Soften the water

If it is impossible to obtain rain or river water, soften the hard water by means of a little borax.

*Hard water which will not dissolve soap
is bad for all ablutions!*

Destructive to the skin

The spirituous essences which are often added to the water for washing the face are very destructive to it. Frequent applications of alcohol dry and harden the skin, and consequently prevent it from nourishing itself with the fresh air or the damp atmosphere.

When the pores have just been opened by the use of water, the skin should be protected from the action of the air, or it will become coarsened and chapped.

Rain water is better than any Turkish bath
for washing the face.
Enveloped from head to foot in a waterproof,
venture outside your dressing room and
encounter the downpour or the soft rain of heaven
without an umbrella, exposing your face to it
during an hour's walk.

The complexion
The colour and texture of the skin cannot be improved much by outward applications.
The complexion depends mainly on the state of the health, or the temperament. We must have recourse to hygiene rather than to cosmetics in order to diminish these faults.

People with very high colour, are generally large eaters and lovers of ease and and luxury and have a great repugnance to healthy exercise.

Choose less succulent food
To lower the tone of a high complexion, people should restrain their appetites, choose less succulent foods and deny themselves some of their comforts, and keep their over-nourished bodies a little under-nourished.
By such a regime, headaches, confusion of mind, and dizziness will disappear.

A pale complexion
When the complexion is muddy, pale, pasty or too white, it can proclaim a bad state of health.
Sometimes a muddy complexion is natural, but more often it denotes a languid circulation.
A pale colour may be due to an indoor life without exercise, from the habit or the necessity of shunning the daylight and the sunshine.

A few precautions
Preserve the face from too much artificial heat.
Cold is unfavourable to dark complexions.
Heat is unfavourable to fair complexions.
Whenever it is possible, avoid a walk going against the wind.

Too much kissing is bad for the complexion.

Sitting up late at night reading novels
is infallible for drawing that terrible network
of crows' feet round the eye.

WRINKLES SMOOTHED OUT

There would be fewer wrinkles if people would correct themselves of certain bad habits.

Frowning
Repeated frowning leaves an indelible mark, in certain straight lines between the eyebrows.

Eyebrows
Lifting the eyebrows at every movement for nothing at all, is done at the cost of long horizontal lines across the forehead, which can make a lady look five years older than she really is!

Smiling artificially
An artificial smile stamps two large creases from the nose to the corners of the mouth.

Face powder
It is an immense mistake to fill up with face powder the lines made by wrinkles!

Beauty secrets to avoid wrinkles

To delay the appearance of wrinkles and
reduce the heaviness of the chin, the face
should be washed and dried from the lower
part to the top.

~

To avoid the dreaded crows' feet, wash the
eyes in the direction from the temple towards
the nose.

~

Make every effort to efface the signs which
late hours and gaieties leave on your face.

~

People who laugh a great deal have little
wrinkles on their cheeks close to the mouth,
but these are rather pleasing.

∾ᴼᴼᴼ∾
Relaxation secrets to avoid wrinkles

When you feel in the blues and worried, go and rest in your dressing room. Stay there till the fatigue has passed off and your good-humour come back. Then you will be able to get up, fresh, beautiful, in an amiable frame of mind, with all your wrinkles smoothed out.

Using this trick you will prolong youth and beauty.

~

Be perfectly still.
If it is possible to take a moment of respite from the accomplishment of daily duties, all ladies are urged to find a little rest for the face, four or five times a day, by shutting the eyes and remaining perfectly still for one, two or five minutes.

Even such short rests from occupations and agitations will greatly retard the ravages that time and life imprint on the face.

SUNBURN RELIEVED

Infallible remedies to try.

It is easy to restore your face from sunburn. Bathe in the evening with a cold infusion of fresh cucumbers cut up in slices in milk. Use butter-milk by itself but a decoction of tansy in butter-milk is more efficacious.

The juice of green grapes
One certain means of getting rid of the burning caused by sea or country air consists in washing with the juice of green grapes.
Wet your bunch of grapes, and sprinkle them lightly with alum, then wrap them up in white paper, and put them to cook under hot charcoal embers. When the grapes are tender, they will be sufficiently done. Take off the paper and squeeze the bunch under a vessel to press and wash your face with this juice.
Do this three times over at intervals of four-and-twenty hours, it is an infallible remedy.

Egg

To remedy the effects of the sun or of the sea air, take the white of an egg beaten into a good froth, bathe the face with it and leave it to dry on the skin for a quarter of an hour, then rinse it off with fresh water. This is done three or four times, and always at night, just before getting into bed.

Drying the face gently with a very fine towel, is essential.

Lemon juice and glycerine

Finally, a mixture of lemon-juice and glycerine in equal parts has good results against the injuries done to our epidermis by the sun and the wind. If the skin will not bear glycerine, it should be replaced by rose-water.

A simple recipe using wine
Very greasy and oily skins will be the better for
being washed with wine about once a fortnight.
If the skin is dark, red wine should be preferred.

ENHANCING THE FACE

Powdering the face must be done artistically ...

Never use any kind of paint; all rouges are bad for the skin, and white paints are dangerous.

The very best
Some of the best things for the skin are:-
- fresh cucumber-juice,
- water in which spinach in flower has been boiled,
- strawberry-juice (perhaps the very best).

For flabby skin
Flabby skins benefit from the following used at intervals of eight days:- Equal parts of milk, and brandy made from corn. Wet the face with this mixture using a soft towel before getting into bed.
The result is not immediate, but after a year the skin will have become firm.

For dry skin

If you have a very dry skin, use only vaseline with a few drops of perfumed oil in it.

A cosmetic made with butter:

At the end of May take a pound of the freshest butter possible (unmixed with salt). Place it in a white basin where the sun will be on it the whole day, but where no dust or dirt can fall on it. When the butter is melted, pour over it plantain-juice. Mix the two together with a wooden spoon. Allow the sun to absorb the plantain-water, and add more juice on six times a day. Continue this till the butter is white. During the last few days add a little orange-flower and rose-water. Anoint your face with this ointment at night and wipe it carefully in the morning.

The use of face powder

Powdering the face must be done artistically and with a light hand, simply enough to give the skin the delightful surface of the peach.

The spectator should be left in doubt as to whether the skin is imperceptibly veiled by a thin cloud of powder, or whether it is the natural bloom.

The puff should be dipped into the powder with caution, so as not to come out too full of powder, which will prevent a wise use of it

Do not wipe the puff across the skin; it should barely touch the face, and then in a succession of small quick taps. Care must be taken not to powder the eyebrows and eyelashes, and to take off any that may have adhered to the lips.

A touch of powder should be put on the whole of the face, except the eyes, eyebrows and lips.

HEALTHY HAIR

Faults may be diminished in the dressing room ...

To be really beautiful, hair should be abundant, fine, and brilliant. But those whose hair is thin, coarse, or lustreless should not despair. These faults may be diminished and the dressing room is the place to make these considerations.

How to Dress the Hair

Nature gives to each face the frame which is most becoming to it, and it is impossible to improve or correct her on this point.

To make the best of whatever hair we possess is to choose the best way of dressing it.

We should not try to curl smooth hair, any more than we should flatten down curly or even wavy hair. It is certain that some faces require the frame which their naturally curly hair gives them.

Do not follow fashion
Women must dress their hair to suit the particular character of their own faces, instead of making themselves ugly by following whatever is the fashion.

Courage
Women ought even to have the courage to allow their hair to become white. All dyes founded on silver or lead are dangerous. Moreover, they only make the hair and complexion ugly.

Snows
Accept the snows the years bring; they harmonise with the countenance which time has given us - and framed in white hair, certain faces become strangely softened and improved. There is both grace and dignity in disdaining to repair the irreparable ravages of time.

Allow your hair freedom

If the hair is drawn too tight, plastered down, or too much twisted, it is no longer an ornament and looks as if the owner is anxious to get rid of it. A certain amount of freedom and abandon should be allowed to the hair.

Fringes

Very deep thick fringes coming down low on the forehead give an animal look to the face; but a few small light little curls on the top of the forehead are very becoming.

Other considerations

Take time to consider the structure of the figure. A small thin woman looks ridiculous if she enlarges her head too much with her hair. If the forehead is high and prominent, and the features large, dragging the hair will be simply hideous. If you make your parting a very little to one side of the head, it will take five years off your age, but a parting quite at the side will make the most delicately moulded face appear masculine.

Avoid eccentricity

Everyone should avoid an eccentric coiffure. The size of the head should never be increased by a mass of false hair. The head will have more refinement and distinction if left to its natural shape and will be more in harmony with the figure to which it belongs.

A worn and elderly-looking woman will find herself wonderfully improved by covering her hair, even if it is still plentiful, with a lace mantilla, which will veil the ravages of time about her face, and will form a graceful frame for it.

How to take care of the hair

The fashion of frizzing the hair, whether with hot irons, pins, or any other artificial means of making it wavy, is a disastrous one.

Be sure that the hair-pins in your dressing room are made of tortoiseshell or gilt wire as these confine the hair without irritating the skin of the head.

Beauty secrets for the hair

It is well to change the way of dressing
the hair for a day or two.

~

If the hair is parted, it should be done
afresh every day.

~

Hair which has the ends cut at every new
moon will grow more abundantly.

~

It is best to sleep with the head uncovered.
Hair that is left free at night will be finer
and more silky.

~

Beware of plaiting the hair under a cap or net;
the more free and separated it is, the more
shining and lustrous it will become.

~

Never wear a starched cap; the starch is sure to
get among the hair and to spoil it.

Brushing

To keep the hair nice, it should be brushed on going to bed at night, as well as when dressing in the daytime, with a soft brush. The best brushes are those with short bristles, and un-bleached. The hair should be disentangled from the extreme end, after having divided it into as many tresses as necessary. If you begin to comb from the roots to the ends, without having sepa-rated the hair into three or four parts, you will do a great deal of damage. You will certainly break it and make it ugly. Walnut-juice is said to make the hair luxuriant.

How to clean the hair

The frequent use of a fine toothcomb is fatal for the hair, especially when it is falling out. Nevertheless, it is necessary to keep the hair and the scalp clean.

An excellent lotion is made as follows:-

Boil 1¾ oz of roots of soap-wort in a pint and a half of water. The preparation should be used warm and the hair and head must be dried quickly with warm towels.

The yolk of an egg is very good for cleaning the hair and helps to make it grow. The skin of the head should be well rubbed with the yolk, and then rinsed with warm water. The white of eggs, well beaten up into a froth, is also one of the simplest and best preparations; it should be used in the same way as the yolks.

Shampooing mixture used in England

A quart of hot or cold water, in which 1 ounce of carbonate of soda has been dissolved and half an ounce of soap cut into small pieces. Add to this some drops of perfumed essence and one ounce of spirits of wine. After washing the hair with this preparation, it should be rinsed with tepid water and then both the head and hair should be rubbed with warm towels till they are dry.

Drying
It is always well to dry the hair rapidly and thoroughly; and after drying, it should be allowed to hang loosely over the shoulders for an hour or two. The hair will get less matted if after shaking it out it is allowed to hang loose over the shoulders while one is dressing and undressing.

The use of flour
White hair (and indeed, some other hair) can be admirably cleaned with flour; it, as well as the skin of the head, should be rubbed with the flour, and then carefully brushed. This is perhaps the best way of all. It is a pity that it is difficult to use it with dark hair, for obvious reasons.

Hair falling out

When the hair falls out without reason, there must be some disease and the same may be said when it splits at the points.

Grief can cause the hair to fall out and get thin. There is no remedy for this but time and forgetfulness and happier days.

Often the hair falls out without any apparent cause; when it does, be sure you are not out of health, - perhaps without knowing it yourself - especially if your hair becomes rough. Watch yourself in this case and find out what the mischief is. Under such circumstances a good treatment for the hair is to soap the scalp and then anoint it, rubbing in well a mixture of castor-oil, of sweet almonds, and of tannin.

Baldness

A man may put up with being bald, but a bald woman is indeed to be pitied.

Either she must take refuge in a wig, or in wearing before her time, lace caps in the house. But the number of women losing their hair increases every day. This is attributed to the curling-irons, which have been too much used; to wigs; to false hair, which has caused the real to fall out; to the woollen fichus thrown over the head to keep it from the cold, either in the house or garden; to the velvet bows worn on the top of the head.

Varying the colour

People do not wait now for their hair to turn white before they dye it; they vary the colour of their hair with their toilette. One day they appear blonde, the next, red or brown. Those who have black hair get it dyed an indelible mahogany tint. When women with fair hair see it getting darker, they immediately try to make it light again with oxidised water, which spoils the texture of the hair.

It is high time to remedy our ways for the sake of future generations. We must go back to simple hair-dressing, without the addition of false hair or crimping-irons!

❦

Secrets for preventing the hair from falling out:-

Lemon juice

Brunettes may stop their locks from falling
out by the application of lemon-juice
to their scalps.

Onions

Take three common onions cleaned and put
into a quart of rum for a whole day and night,
the onions are then taken out, and the rum
used to rub the scalp with every other day.
The slight odour evaporates in a few minutes.

Decoction of the leaves of walnuts

Make a decoction of the leaves of the walnut
in water and wet the scalp every night by
means of a sponge.

Sage-tea

Tepid sage-tea is recommended on condition
that the head is well dried with warm towels.

The following pomade is recommended for hair which is falling out:
- *5 parts of tincture of jaborandi*
- *3 parts of lanoline*
- *20 parts of glycerine*

Mix with the help of a little soft-soap; the head to be rubbed every night with a little of this pomade on the end of your finger.

A sanctuary

The clever woman makes of her dressing room a sanctuary where no one, not even her husband (above all not her husband) may cross the threshold, where she may give herself up to the service of beauty and hair-dressing.

Dry hair

Some hair is so dry that it cannot do without pomade for fear of breaking it. Recommended is oil of vaseline, perfumed according to preference. If other oils are preferred, they can be prepared at home. Care should be taken to clarify the oil used and for this it must undergo a preliminary preparation.

A fragrant pomade

To make a pomade, take 3 ounces of the grease prepared in the best manner, 2 ounces of marrow and 1 ounce of sweet-almond oil; before these substances are quite stiff and cold, perfume them with 3 minims of essence of bergamot and 1 drachm of essence of violet.

Some people use water instead of pomade; nothing is worse for the hair. The habit of using the saliva to smooth the hair is a disgusting and often a dangerous one!

How to clean brushes

There is nothing better than ammonia for cleaning hair-brushes; it does not soften the bristles as soap and soda do. Put a teaspoonful of ammonia in a quart of water; dip the brush into this, preserving the ivory or wooden backs if possible. An immersion of a few seconds will suffice. The brush should then be dipped in clear water and dried in the open air, but not in the sun.

How to clean combs and brushes

Combs must never be washed. They can be cleaned with a tightly-stretched string or with a card, by sticking the teeth into cotton-wool, or by using a little flat hard brush, or any of the implements invented by hairdressers for the purpose. There are special brushes for brushing out the combs every time they are used.

The greatest neatness is necessary for all implements used for hair-dressing.

AN ATTRACTIVE MOUTH

*Many ladies remain pretty from knowing how to
preserve the freshness of their lips
and the charm of their smile.*

When you have eaten onion, swallow a cup of
black coffee immediately after. Coffee is an an-
tidote to the atrocious odour which that bulb
communicates to the respiratory organs. As for
garlic, let no one ever touch it!

Smooth lips
If your lips are not rough, they will always have
a certain freshness and smoothness, which in itself is a charm.

Beauty secrets for the lips

To be beautiful, the lips should be the red of raspberries, soft and not chapped.

~

Red lips are incompatible with certain temperaments. Some ladies must resign themselves to pale-coloured lips.

~

Many women bite their lips on entering a room, to make them red. But, besides the fact that the colour thus obtained only lasts a few seconds, the habit of biting the lips makes them sore and inclined to chap.

~

If your lips are naturally dry and rough, rub them a little every night with equal parts of water and glycerine.

Beauty secrets for the lips

Do not pass your tongue over your lips. This is against the rules of polite society, and the dampness is not good for them.

~

Extravagant laughter on all occasions must not be indulged in by those who wish to keep their lips pretty.

~

Avoid contortions of the mouth in speaking, in particular do not draw in and push out the lips when you speak.

~

Excessive laughter and contortions of the face will disfigure the mouth and bring on premature old age.

~

To reduce lips that are too thick, rubbing with tannin may be tried.

PERFECT TEETH

It is certain that nothing increases the charm of a smile so much and nothing is so necessary to it, as a double row of perfectly good white teeth.

Pretty teeth are essential to the beauty of a lady, and good teeth - which are almost always pretty - are indispensable to health.

Charm
The loss of the teeth brings on old age before its time. Guard jealously what nature has given you. Take care of your teeth and preserve the purity of the breath, which is a charm above others.

Cleaning
Cleaning the teeth is the surest way of combating the causes of their ruin. They should be cleaned by careful brushing night and morning and it is an excellent thing to rinse out the mouth after every meal. By degrees the gums will be accustomed to more energetic friction.

A decoction of myrrh, tannin, and oakbark would be an excellent wash for tender gums, as it acts as an astringent.

Lemon also has a very good action on tender or even ulcerated gums. Dip a camel's hair brush into the lemon juice and tap the affected parts with it, without touching the teeth.

A summer cleaner

In the summer season the most delicious and the best dentifrice is the strawberry. It cleans the teeth to perfection. It should be bruised on the brush, the teeth rubbed with it, and then rinsed out with tepid water. An infusion made with the petals of the pink procures one of the best elixirs also durng the summer. The pink is an antiseptic.

You should also eat a small crust of bread at the end of every meal, after the dessert.

Tartar

In spite of all washes and dentifrices, tartar will form, even on the most carefully kept teeth. People subject to gout and rheumatism will find tartar forming on their teeth to some extent, in spite of all their care.

Energetic brushing will at least in some degree prevent, delay or sometimes even destroy, the appearance of tartar. Take a little alum on your brush (which should be very slightly wet) and brush your teeth with it every morning for three or four days at a time.

Rinse your mouth with honey and water to correct any strong astringent.

Salt

There is one occasion on which salt may be of great use. After having a tooth extracted, the mouth is filled with salt and water, there need be no fear of haemorrage.

Bad foods

Some foods, such as sugar, bonbons, and confectionery, are bad for the teeth. It is said that dates and radishes, because they are acid, are also bad for the teeth. Figs, like sugar, weaken the teeth, and oils and greasy substances do them no good.

Breathing

You should breathe through the nose, especially in cold weather.

If you breathe through the mouth in winter, you expose your teeth to a current of air at a much lower temperature than that of your body. All sensible people will understand that it is bad for the teeth to breathe through the mouth or to sleep with the mouth open.

Toothache

When you suffer from toothache, mistrust the ordinary remedies that are recommended. Cloves and essence of cinnamon, etc. may ease your pain, but it is said that they destroy your teeth.

Go at once to the dentist and if you are obliged to delay doing so, use only such remedies as are harmless.

Secrets to relieve toothache

Roll some parsley with a little salt up into a small ball and put it into the ear on the side where the pain is.

~

Paint the cheek with lemon-juice, or apply a hot flannel to the face.

~

A scanty diet and warm baths will sometimes calm the toothache.

~

If the teeth have been hurt by an acid, seltzer-water will reduce the irritation.

~

A strong solution of bicarbonate of soda is another remedy for toothache. Rinse the mouth well with this solution and apply a little bicarbonate of soda to the teeth and gums with a brush.

Recipes for clearing the voice
If a slight irritation of the throat spoils the sweet-
ness and musical sonority of your voice, gargle
with salt-and-water (common salt). It is very
good to inhale the steam of hot milk in which
figs have been boiled, if you want to mellow the
tone of the voice. Fumigations are also excellent. Mix a little powdered amber and myrrh
together, put them on a red-hot shovel, and inhale the smoke. An infusion of male veronica
with a little sugar-candy is also recommended.
A glassful should be taken before breakfast.

BEAUTY IN THE EYES

In the sanctuary of your dressing room, study your eyes and learn to improve them. Eyes are only really beautiful if they reflect good and wholesome thoughts and noble sentiments.

Some ladies have eyes which are so beautiful that they make one forget any irregularity in the features, and even other physical defects. They exercise a fascinating charm.

The language of the eyes
Their power does not lie in their colour; it matters not whether they have borrowed the tint of the corn-flower or the flash of the black diamond, whether they reflect the June sky or hide their velvety softness under long lashes; it is the expression which makes them beautiful.

They must reflect a soul tender, sweet, loyal and sure, ardent and loving. The inner being must show itself in the eyes.

A frank direct look

The eye should be long, almond-shaped and fringed with long lashes. Some wish them to be gentle, others demand that they shall flash. Above all things, the eye should open wide, with a fine, frank, direct look, a look which is not afraid to meet the regard of others. It is not attractive to have a furtive, suspicious look!

Feelings

The most beautiful eyes are those which express all feelings sincerely. Some are tender and sweet, but they can flash like lightning in moments of indignation or enthusiasm. These eyes can hide nothing; you may have confidence in those who have them.

Let jealousy, cunning, or envy depict themselves
in the eyes and they will at once lose all their
charm and power!

Eyes which take hold of one's heart

Two people that love each other can speak with their eyes and have no need of any other language. There are some eyes so splendid in expression, so admirable in their limpid clearness, that they take hold of one's heart and soul, and it is impossible to resist them. There are eyes so powerful that they almost hypnotise one.

Care of the eyes

The greatest beauty of the eyes lies in their expression, but if they are to keep all their seductive fascination, they must not be red, inflamed, tired or without eyelashes.

Something in your eye

Never rub your eyes, if you do not want to have red eyelids. Even if something gets into your eye, do not irritate it by trying to get rid of the intruder by violent measures. Close your eyes quickly, and wait patiently thus even for a quarter of an hour, if necessary. The natural watering of the eye will expel the foreign substance.

Red eyes
If your eyes are red from the wind, bathe them in tepid water with a little common salt in it.

Lamps
Lamps should always have large shades on them. It is dangerous to the sight to look at the sun or at the centre of an electric light. Gas, candles, and ordinary lamps should all be subdued by screens and smoked glasses.

Reading and other close work
The light should come from the side, not in front. You should write on tinted paper and only read books and newspapers that are well-printed. Avoid stooping too much in reading, writing or sewing. It is bad for the sight to read in the train, or while driving and walking.

Sitting up late - and artificial light - makes the eyes red and tired.

Rest the eyes

However strong your eyes may be, grant them a little rest after two hours of continuous work, whether the pen or the needle. If they are weak, do not occupy them much with any work which involves fixing them on minute objects. Do not write, read, sew, or do anything which demands an effort when the light is insufficient. Whatever work you are doing, close the eyes every now and then for an instant. Let them wander to a distance, too, at intervals.

Colours

The most restful colours for the eyes are green and blue. Do not surround yourself with very bright colours. Red is blinding. Choose soft shades, very much blended, in hangings, stuffs and wall-papers. Very dark shades are unsuitable either for decoration or furniture and strong contrasts are equally tiring to the eyes.

Protection from the fire and other bright light

Do not amuse yourself by watching the play of the flames in the grate. A screen is a necessity, even if you are sitting at one side of the fire. White walls on which the light is vividly reflected, the snow, or roads whitened by the rays of the sun in summer, are very fatiguing to the eyes.

Wide-brimmed hats, shading the forehead well, are the best head-dress for the summer, as they protect the eyes from the fierce light of the sun's rays.

෨ଡ଼ଡ଼ଡ଼

Beauty secrets for the eyes

Use a plain piece of glass on the page when
reading and in this way delay the use of
spectacles. Under the glass, the paper of the
book or newspaper is less staringly white, and
the characters appear more distinct.

~

Use magnifying-glasses, microscopes, and
eye-glasses as sparingly as possible and take
off your glasses whenever you can do without
them, when out walking, talking, etc.

~

Never rub your eyes on awakening, and prevent little children from acquiring this habit.

~

Bathe your eyes pretty often, especially
morning and evening.

~

An infusion of weak black tea is good for
bathing sore eyes.

Beauty secrets for the eyes

Avoid all eye-washes that have not been
prescribed by a good doctor or oculist.

~

If your eyelids are inflamed, wash them with
rose- and plantain-water. Strawberry juice
well strained through a cloth is also
very beneficial.

~

Elderflower water can be used for the pricking
one sometimes feels in the eyes.

~

The juice of chervil and of lettuce is also
refreshing when the eyes are irritable.

~

The evening is the best time for bathing
the eyes.

THE EYE LASHES

... thick and long ...

To be beautiful and protect the eyes, eye lashes should be long and thick. Some women have the points of their eye lashes cut, to make them thick and long. Rubbing the eyes is a bad habit and can make the lashes fall out. The blackening of the lashes cannot be recommended, in spite of the attraction it may lend to the eye.

THE EYEBROWS

... an air of serenity ...

Bushy eyebrows give something fierce to the face and thin combs keep them in good order. Fine arched eyebrows give an air of serenity to the countenance. Rather thick eyebrows are becoming to the eyes. Scanty eyebrows, are a real defect. Bathe them every morning in cold water and rub with petroleum jelly to make them grow.

THE NOSE

... chiselled in the most exquisite manner ...

Your nose may be chiselled in the most exquisite manner, but if the roses of your cheeks have spread over it, you will wish that instead of your inflamed Greek nose you had a common snub one, if only it were quite white.

Abnormal redness

Redness of the nose often proceeds from a kind of congestion. Such persons must abstain from ham, or pork under any form, meat, bacon, and and also from salt meats or highly-spiced foods.

Never touch your nostrils with your fingers

Redness also comes from a bad state of the nostrils; in that case, wash with hot water (cold will increase the redness). Never touch your nostrils with your fingers. Sniff up a little hot water, and eject it gently. Cream spread on the irritated part will protect it against the effects of the open air.

Small black spots

The little black spots with which many noses (and sometimes cheeks) are spotted, should be squeezed between your fingers.

Washing with fresh water is advisable; also frictioning with diluted glycerine. Friction with soft-soap is also recommended.

The science of rhinoplasty

This science, which concerns the nose, has made such progress that it is possible now to modify, even to change, the shape of the nose. However, to persons afflicted with a large nose, the following is suggested as a means of diminishing its size. To do this, wear a *pince-nez*, without glasses in it, at night and in the day-time whenever you are alone.

If the nose is a little on one side, or deviates from the central line, it must be blown exclusively on the defective side until it has become straight.

*Wearing the stays too tight may also be
the cause of a red nose, in which case
the clothes should be worn loosely.*

THE EAR

... charming little ears ...

It is necessary to clean the exterior of the ear very carefully. Many scrupulously neat people, (from not being able to see this part of their body) do not succeed in clearing all the little corners of the ear from dust and other matters that soil it.

The most charming little ears, the shape of a bean and lined with rose-colour, seem profaned by want of care in cleaning them. Instead of being delightful to look at, they present an almost repulsive aspect. If this is so with a pretty ear, what must it be in a commonplace or ugly one?

Delicate Ears

If your ears are at all delicate, it is bad for the hearing for your feet to be cold. Beware of the damp for your extremities and never sit with your back to an open window.

A LADYLIKE HAND

It takes five generations of leisure to possess an elegant and aristocratic hand.

A white and delicate hand can be achieved even if we occupy ourselves with our households and do gardening, but we must take some trouble.

Care of the hands

The roughest hands may be made soft and smooth by a few minutes' care every night in the dressing room before going to bed.

Your dressing room must contain a small, but very inexpensive, store, namely,

a nail-brush,
a pumice-stone,
a box of powdered borax,
a bottle of ammonia,
a pot for fine water sand,
a lemon,
glycerine.

Beauty secrets for the hands

If hard skin is forming on the inside of the
hand, rub the place patiently as necessary with
pumice-stone. This is important to preserve
the softness and delicacy of touch.

~

If the lines on the palm become filled with
grease, they must be perfectly cleaned.

~

When the hands are absolutely clean, rub them
with dry oatmeal and wear gloves at night.

~

Lemon-juice, sand or borax will serve well for
removing stains.

~

If you wet a little salt with lemon-juice,
there is no stain that this simple mixture
will not obliterate.

Stains of tar
A piece of fresh orange- or lemon-peel (if you have it at the moment) will take tar well by rubbing with the outside of the peel. The hands should be wiped at once to dry them.

Stains of ink
Ripe tomatoes or strawberries, a sorrel-leaf, or a little milk, are all nearly as good as lemon-juice for removing ink-stains from the hands.

Stains of potatoes
If you should happen to peel potatoes, be sure that your hands are very dry for this work and that you do not wash them immediately after it. By taking this slight precaution, the hands will not be stained by the juice of the tuber.

Stains of fruit and vegetables
After peeling fruit and certain vegetables a little, wet the hands with water and then lemon-juice to restore the hands to a proper state.

Fat hands

If your hands are rather fat, do not wear tight sleeves. The pressure and discomfort to the arm will only make the hand swell. A tight cuff is as unsuitable to the large hand as a low heel is to a large foot. If your fingers are square at the ends, you may narrow them a little by pinching and squeezing the tips.

Chapped hands

Chapped hands are uncomfortable; this will usually happen in winter.

Some persons only wash their hands
in warm water to keep them clean
during the day and at night, wet them
with glycerine and rose-water
and sleep in gloves.

Allow relaxation time
Women who look after the plants in their rooms, who comb their hair and attend to household duties, wash their hands frequently; and as their time is precious to them, they do everything quickly and in a hurry.

Just a few moments
Sacrifice a few moments to dry your hands thoroughly. When the hands have been dried with all possible care, they may be rubbed before the fire till they are quite soft and flexible. Cold water should not be used for washing the hands; it makes them more liable to chap; neither is very hot water good for them.

Thin skin
People with very thin skins should be extremely careful to dry their hands well. They should also cover them with a little cold cream or vaseline, and wipe them again after applying it.

❧◎◦

Beauty secrets for chapped hands

In your dressing room, where you will not be
disturbed, wash your hands well in warm
water.   Take some vaseline, lard, or tallow,
and cover the hands with this.
Whichever you choose, use it abundantly.

Rub your hands well, twisting them about,
rubbing between the fingers for a good while,
until they have become soft and do not feel
sore if you knock them against anything hard.

Divest the hands of the grease you have
rubbed on them and wash them with
good soap and warm water.
It is necessary to change the water several times.

Rub your hands with the following mixture:-
Glycerine, soft water, and eau de cologne,
in equal parts.
*The hands will be very soft, and not the least
sticky, as might be supposed.*

Another remedy

Take one handful of very pure linseedmeal,
One teaspoonful of oil of bitter almonds.
Mix these two ingredients well together, then
add warm water enough to make a light bouillie
of them. Plunge your hands into this liquid and
rub them in it for about a quarter of an hour,
then rinse them in tepid water.

Almond remedy

Bitter-almond oil is prepared by mixing half a
drachm of essence of bitter almonds with one
pint of olive oil.
The last recipe may be used not only for chapped
hands, but for getting rid of chilblains that are
not broken; this is another of the ills of winter.

CHILBLAINS
ON THE HANDS AND THE FEET

*Chilblains are even more to be dreaded
than a chapped skin ...*

A weak constitution or bad food predispose one to this affection. Sufferers should walk a great deal, exercise their hands, rub with alcoholic preparations the parts where the chilblains are not broken and keep their hands and feet warm. It is often in mild and damp winters that certain constitutions suffer most from chilblains.

There are many remedies for this unbearable ailment which spoils the prettiest hands and feet in the world.

*People with a slow circulation should wear gloves
the moment the temperature begins to fall.*

Remedies for chilblain sufferers

Crush lily bulbs and put them into a vessel
containing walnut oil. Apply this under fine
cloths to the parts affected.

~

Brittany honey will heal open chilblains.
Put on the sore places and cover with
fine white linen.

~

Wash ulcerated chilblains with tincture of
myrrh very much diluted with tepid water.

~

Steep any broken chilblains several times in a
little spirits of salt weakened by much water.

~

Before getting into bed, put your hands into
mustard and water, then apply a liniment
composed of camphor and oil of turpentine.

Remedies for chilblain sufferers

Constipation should be avoided and all
the functions of the body should be kept
in good order.

~

Chilblains may be prevented if the hands are
rubbed with a slice of lemon after every wash.

~

Wash your hands two or three times a week in
salt and water.

~

Cut two turnips in slices and pass them
through a strainer with three large spoonfuls of
very pure axunge. Apply this at night and
cover with a white cloth.

~

Make a decoction of a pinch of laurel-leaves
in a quart of water. Wash the hands every
morning with this, a little warmed.

Beautiful nails are looked upon as a precious gift.
They should have a white crescent at the root and
they should be as rosy as the dawn.

CARE OF THE NAILS

... a gentle curve ...

The ugliest nails can be improved by taking the trouble to push back the hard skin that grows at the base. This should only be done after soaping the hands in warm water. The edges of the nail should also be filed in a gentle curve, following the outline of the finger end. The surface of the nail should then be polished.

Just one hour
One hour in the week given up to the care of the nails would keep them in good order. Nothing is better than a lemon for cleaning the nails; stick the ends of the fingers down into it, and turn them in it again and again. Lemon also prevents the skin from growing up over the nails. It is very good for the little loose jags of skin which only form at the base of badly-kept nails.

Cream and other implements for the nails
The use of cold cream at night is good for the nails; it softens and keeps them from breaking.

Essential implements to keep in your dressing room for taking care of the nails:-

one ordinary nailbrush,
one smaller brush,
a file,
a polisher,
curved scissors - two pairs.

It is not possible to cut the nails of the right hand with scissors meant to cut those of the left.

WELL-FITTED GLOVES

Gloves too tight do not wear well and true elegance should always be blended with good sense.

The dressing room is the place to select and care for your gloves.

Air your gloves
Never pull off your gloves from the ends of the fingers. Turn inside out. If you do not air gloves in this way, they will shrink. Gloves should *not* be rolled up inside each other. They should be stretched out in a box or perfumed sachet.

Light gloves
Light gloves should lie between two pieces of white flannel. Clean with flour if slightly soiled.

Black gloves
Black gloves are renovated by mixing a few drops of good black ink in a teaspoonful of olive-oil. Apply it with a feather and dry them in the sun.

New gloves properly fitted ...

In first fitting a pair of new gloves -

Insert the four fingers in the glove,
turn back the body of the glove over the hand,
when the fingers are quite in, introduce
the thumb with care.
Lean your elbow on your knee for support.

Turn back the glove on the wrist,
button the second button first,
going on thus to the top,
then come back to the first button.
You will find that it will button easily.

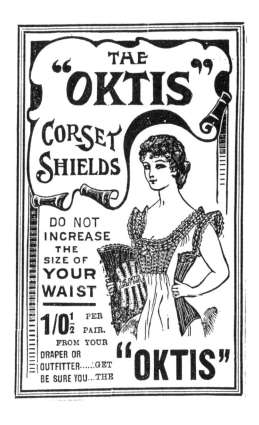

AN ELEGANT FOOT

... in harmonious proportion to the body ...

When a foot is well made, the boots and shoes wear well, and the walk is generally harmonious and graceful. But the most charming foot may be disfigured by a boot that is too short or too narrow. An ugly foot will become still worse if the owner tries to diminish its proportions by compressing it.

Warning
Never try to make your foot smaller; you will only thicken it. The foot should be in harmonious proportion to the body.
A rather long foot is the most elegant, as it appears narrow. It is absurd to compress a wide foot; you only subject it to excruciating pain and lose the ease and grace of your walk.
No other boot except leather is fit for winter wear, as the ankles must be protected from the cold.

Trying on boots and shoes
If at all possible, have boots and shoes made for you. If you do buy them ready-made, try them on in the evening. You should always try on your boots and shoes in the evening, when your feet are tired, and with comparatively thick stockings on. You will then find that you have plenty of room in your boots when your feet are fresh and you have put on very fine stockings.

Recognise a well-cut shoe
A well-cut pair of shoes may be known by the following signs. When the shoes are placed beside each other, they should only touch each other at the toes and heels. The soles should follow the line of the foot, so that it can rest its whole width on it comfortably.

Never take long walks with quite new boots on.
Wear them in the house first for a few days
and then when you go out for a short time.

Secrets for choosing boots and shoes ...

If the foot is narrow and long, the boot
should be short in the toe, laced or buttoned
in the front.

~

An ornament on the top of the shoe diminishes
the length of the foot in appearance.

~

A short fat foot demands a long boot,
buttoned or laced at the side.

~

A very flat foot requires rather high heels.

~

The wellington boot is altogether
unacceptable.

~

The kid boot should reach higher than
the ankle.

~

A black boot is the only really pretty one.

~

A white shoe enlarges and widens the foot.

Secrets for choosing boots and shoes ...

An open shoe may be worn in colours which are forbidden in a boot. All the same, it is well to choose a colour that matches the dress, but is a little darker.

~

Black shoes and black stockings diminish both the length and breadth of the foot.

~

Women with thick ankles should wear stockings with embroidery high up on the sides in the length, not across the width: it will make the ankles appear smaller.

~

When strong boots are worn with a light and elegant toilette, it is a sign of the very worst taste.

If you cannot have nice boots and shoes, you should wear quiet and simple dresses.

How to take care of the feet

The feet should be washed every day and rubbed with a pumice-stone, all thickness of the skin will disappear.

The daily repetition of a foot-bath does not suit everybody. It has the bad effect of making the feet too tender.

After washing your feet and while they are still wet, rub the sole with dry salt and then wipe them vigorously. This will strengthen them.

Warm your feet by walking.

Foot-warmers

Foot-warmers of all kinds are bad. They make you likely to have varicose veins in the legs. When you travel in very cold weather, wear over your shoes long stockings in the train or carriage, to prevent chilblains on your feet. Snow-boots are even better, but they are more difficult to carry about when you take them off on leaving the carriage.

Tired and swollen feet

If the feet are tired from long standing, a bath of salt and water is excellent for them. Put a handful of common salt in four quarts of water, as hot as can be borne without pain. Place your feet into this and with your hand splash the water over your legs up to the knees.

It is also advisable, when the feet are swollen from a long walk or much standing, to bathe them in water in which charcoal has been boiled. The water should be strained through a cloth before putting the feet into it. Swelling and fatigue will both disappear radidly.

*A bath of lime-tree flowers is
very soothing to tired feet.*

Corns

What an infliction! Happily, they are not without a remedy. A shoe that is too wide is almost as destructive as one that is too narrow. If the foot is not properly supported, it will rub against the leather and this friction predisposes to corns.

Remedies for corns

Rid yourself of a recently grown corn by rubbing it with pumice-stone. While the corn is still tender, it can be got the better of by applying wool dipped in leaves of red geranium steeped in oil. Raw onion bruised softens the corn. A poultice of the crumb of bread, steeped in vinegar for thirty minutes will cure a new corn in one night.

Bunions

Bunions, particularly affect the big and little toes, and sometimes the instep and can be cured in several ways -

*If bunions are on the instep, high heels
should be at once renounced.*

Remedies for bunions
If the bunion is inflamed, cover it with a poultice and wear easy slippers. Then anoint the suffering part with an ointment composed of 7 parts of iodine mixed with 30 of lard.

Take a piece of wash-leather and make a hole in it large enough for the bunion, put it on the bad place and cover it with oiled silk. Over this silk rub the bunion twice a day with the ointment of iodine and axunge.

Cramp in the foot
If the toes are not perfectly free in the boot or shoe, the constraint gives rise to the most horrible cramp.

A remedy for cramp
The cramp which so many people are subject to at night is prevented by raising the pillow. Place under the feet at the head of the bed a block the thickness of two bricks. Relief is immediate.

∞⟨⟩∞
Useful secrets for comfortable boots

When you come in with your leather boots
wet, take them off at once, and have them
filled with dry hay. This absorbs the damp
rapidly and fills out the boots and so prevents
them from stiffening and losing their shape.

The next day the hay is taken out and may be
dried for another occasion or thrown away.
*By stuffing the boots with paper you will
obtain exactly the same result.*
Above all, avoid putting them near the fire.
~

Paraffin softens boots that have stiffened from
a wetting and restores all their suppleness.
~

Strong boots can be softened by exposure to
broom-smoke and by rubbing with olive-oil
and lard. They will thus be much more comfortable, last twice as long and will protect the
feet better from the cold and damp.

*Satin petticoats frayed and ragged - and others
encrusted with mud - appear under superb gowns
when these were held up!*

THE CHEMISE AND OTHER UNDERCLOTHING

Women of refined taste never gave up white linen or even simple calico, which can be easily washed.

A true woman, who has the instinct of elegance will not be content with having fresh and dainty only her outside garments, but her underclothes will be just as correct, in quite as good condition and even more scrupulously neat.

Simple underclothing but clean

Dressmakers say that women in society are not ashamed to send them for patterns, bodices which are horribly soiled and greasy and which show they have never undergone the little repairs. Undergarments may be simple, but they should be as gracefully cut as possible.

Rather than have only a scanty stock,
it is better to have less expensive material
and the necessary quantity.

A certain sobriety
A virtuous woman has a repugnance to excessive luxury in her underclothing. She does not like too much lace or embroidery. She has them trimmed, of course, but with a certain sobriety, she likes them to be elegant, but she denies herself the over-richness of trimming.

*What can be more refreshing
than to put on fresh linen?*

The corset for the stout woman
The corset is absolutely necessary for the stout woman. It controls the exuberance of her bodice, and it is impossible for a fat woman to have any pretence to being well-dressed without it.

The corset for the thin woman
The corset supports the petticoats, which would otherwise lie too heavily on the waist and a very thin woman will have no style without its help.

Support to the bust
The corset serves as a support to the bust, the fibres of which would become distended and it would soon fall too low!

The corset must always be absolutely clean.

Do not tie garters too tightly
To avoid varicose veins, women should take care not to garter too tightly. They will, of course, not wear their garters below the knee.
Exercise develops the legs and enlarges the calf.

Garters
Garters should be carefully chosen. Always be clean and fresh and never ragged or shabby. There is an advantage as well as from that of refinement, in not buying cheap and common garters, which will not last and will hold up the stockings very badly.

Garters may be simple, but they
must be irreproachable.

How to fasten stockings

Everyone cannot bear a garter as tight as it should be. Their legs swell under pressure and varicose veins form. In this case, the stockings should be fastened to the stays by ribbons (suspenders).

Avoid a catastrophe

Accidents might happen; if the ribbon, which must be well stretched to hold up the stocking, were to break, down comes the stocking over the heel - what a catastrophe! The advice is to wear at the same time a garter (not at all tight, but sufficiently so to hold up the stocking) in case of accidents, until the damage can be repaired in the privacy of your dressing room.

The most humble servant-maid who is a little civilised buys elastic garters with buckles.

The chemise

If the chemise, the drawers, the little under-petticoat, and the slip-bodice could all be made to match, it would be in charmingly good taste.

The night chemise

Neither the flannel nor the linen which has been worn by day should be kept on at night. It is cleaner and more healthy to change.

The night chemise should reach down to the feet and should have long sleeves.

Dressing in the morning

In the calm of your dressing room, take time to consider the day's plans. Make the appropriate choice of clothing, before beginning your morning routine.

The face should be wiped with a fine towel and an entire bath taken, followed by friction.

Preparations for the afternoon

Those who work in their households as well as those who only superintend them, should dress themselves with perfect neatness and care as nicely as possible. It is as well to change the undergarments - stockings, petticoats, etc. - as well as the dress, for the afternoon.

Undressing for the night

Some people prefer taking their bath at night; in any case, both night and morning the body demands ablutions to refresh and clean it.

The clothes we take off

Never put up directly, neither in drawers nor in cupboards, any of the clothes you take off. Open them out, or hang them up in an airy place for at least an hour. Then, after having brushed and folded them, have them put by.

The clothes which cannot be washed should be occasionally hung out in the air for a day and turned inside out.

MORE COPPER BEECH GIFT BOOKS ...

'Tonics Restoratives & Money-Saving Hints'

KITCHEN COSMETICS
BEAUTY FROM YOUR PANTRY
How to have a smooth clear complexion - and
other potions and preparations for natural beauty.
Original ingredients from yesterday's kitchens.

APPEARANCES
HOW TO KEEP THEM UP
ON A LIMITED INCOME
Use the housekeeping money wisely,
train the cook well, how to shop,
how to plan a modest dinner party.

DAINTY DISHES
FOR SLENDER INCOMES
Do not be constrained by your budget.
Money-saving ideas, well-tried recipes and
'hints worth remembering'.

THE SERVANTLESS HOUSEHOLD
HOW TO COPE – SOME POLITE ADVICE
How to keep the house in order without the
benefit of staff. Maintain high standards and
be prepared for anything!

THE ETIQUETTE COLLECTION

Etiquette for ~
CHOCOLATE LOVERS
COFFEE LOVERS
THE CHILDREN
THE CHAUFFEUR
DRESS
AN ENGLISH TEA
GENTLEMEN
LOVE & COURTSHIP
MOTORING
NAMING THE BABY
POLITENESS
ENGLISH PUDDINGS
A TRADITIONAL CHRISTMAS
THE TRAVELLER
THE WELL DRESSED MAN
WINE LOVERS

~ good manners for every occasion!
For your free catalogue containing these and other titles write to:

Copper Beech Publishing Ltd
P O Box 159 East Grinstead
Sussex England RH19 4FS
www.copperbeechpublishing.co.uk

Copper Beech Gift Books
www.copperbeechpublishing.co.uk